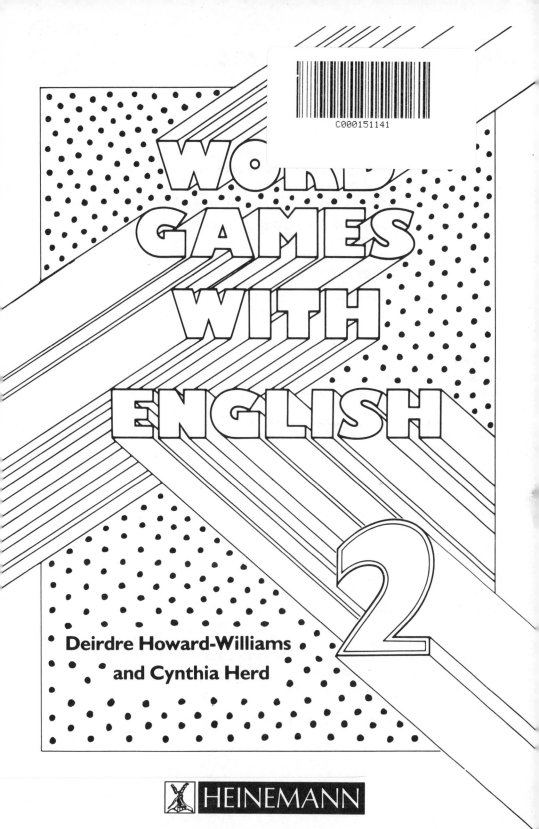

WORD GAMES WITH ENGLISH 2

**Deirdre Howard-Williams
and Cynthia Herd**

HEINEMANN

Heinemann Games Series

Titles in this series include:

Word Games with English 1   Deirdre Howard-Williams & Cynthia Herd   0 435 28380 4
Word Games with English 2   Deirdre Howard-Williams & Cynthia Herd   0 435 28381 2
Word Games with English 3   Deirdre Howard-Williams & Cynthia Herd   0 435 28382 0
Word Games with English Plus   Deirdre Howard-Williams & Cynthia Herd   0 435 28379 0

Play Games With English Book 1   Colin Granger   0 435 28060 0
Teacher's Book 1   0 435 28061 9
Play Games With English Book 2   Colin Granger   0 435 28062 7
Teacher's Book 2   0 435 28063 5

English Puzzles 1   Doug Case   0 435 28280 8
English Puzzles 2   Doug Case   0 435 28281 6

Heinemann International
a division of Heinemann Educational Books Ltd
Halley Court, Jordan Hill, Oxford OX2 8EJ

OXFORD   LONDON   EDINBURGH   MADRID   ATHENS   BOLOGNA
MELBOURNE   SYDNEY   AUCKLAND   IBADAN   NAIROBI   GABORONE   HARARE
KINGSTON   PORTSMOUTH (NH)   SINGAPORE

ISBN 0 435 28381 2

© Deirdre Howard-Williams and Cynthia Herd 1986
First published 1986

Illustrated by Tony Kenyon
Phototypesetting by T & R Filmsetters Ltd, Willesden, London NW10 2DH
Printed and bound in Great Britain by
Thomson Litho Ltd, East Kilbride, Scotland

90   91   92   93   94   95   10   9   8   7   6   5

About this book

Word Games With English is a series of 3 books of carefully graded language activities designed to stimulate learners to practise, activate and extend their English vocabulary.

Pedagogical Basis

● Book 2, for post-beginners, is closely based on the vocabulary designated by the Council of Europe for Threshold level, which represents a level of general language ability.

● A number of words have also been added from grades 2 and 3 of the *Cambridge English Lexicon* (R. Hindmarsh), based on 4 major frequency counts.

● There are over 1,000 lexical items in this book, allowing the learner to deal with most everyday situations and providing a sound basis for further study.

Presentation

● The vocabulary concentrates on essential topic areas: personal identification, trade and occupation, entertainment, travel, health and welfare, education, food and drink, services etc.

● The games provide an introduction to language forms: word building, prepositional phrases, abbreviations, punctuation etc.

● Each page is highly visual. The words are contextualised and illustrations help to make the meanings clear.

● Each game calls for the learner's active participation.

● There is built-in revision and recycling of certain lexical items in different contexts.

● The book is suitable for all ages, for teaching and testing, for class and group work and for varied further exploitation.

● There is a full answer key and word list enabling the book to be used also for self-study and revision.

How to use this book

1   Read what to do carefully.

2   Write your answers on a piece of paper or in the book.

3   Look at the back of the book for the answers.

There is also a list of words at the end of the book for your reference.

Contents

	Page		
About this book	iii	Christmas Shopping	24
How to use this book	iv	Crossword 2	26
Quick Service	1	Prepositions 1	27
Around the World	2	Person or Thing?	28
Doubles 1	3	Nationalities	29
Sports	4	Word Families 2	30
Station Signs	5	Help in the Home	31
Word Families 1	6	Thieves	32
Map Reading	7	Make a Choice	33
The Application Form	8	Shopping Centre	34
A Picnic in the Country	9	Doubles 2	35
Abbreviations 1	10	Thank You	36
Opposites	11	Work for Us!	37
Hotel Signs	12	Odd One Out 2	38
Crossword 1	14	Prepositions 2	39
OO and EE	15	Travel Quiz	40
Masculine and Feminine	16	Where does it Go?	41
Clothes	17	Crossword 3	42
Odd One Out 1	18	Prefixes & Suffixes	43
Money	19	In the Press	44
At the Theatre	20	Books	45
What Would You Say?	21	The Word Snake	46
Abbreviations 2	22	Answers	47
Emergency	23	Word List	53

To Jean-François Argenson and Irene Margaret Wade

QUICK SERVICE

This waiter is carrying 8 different dishes for 8 different people. The number on each dish is the number of the order. Can you fill in his orders?

For example:

roast pork and peas   grilled lamb, mushrooms and peas
spaghetti with tomato sauce   ham salad and bread roll
fried bacon and sausages   strawberries and cream
boiled beef, carrots and cabbage   vanilla ice-cream and pears

AROUND THE WORLD

Can you recognise these countries?
Can you spell them correctly?

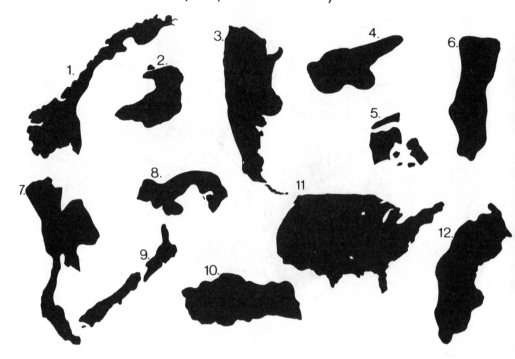

For example:

1. RYNOAW   Norway

2. ASEWL

3. TANGRIANE

4. PYSUCR

5. KANDERM

6. APUGRTOL

7. HALITNAD

8. APAMNA

9. EWN LAZENDA

10. YURTEK

11. IDENUT TESAST

12. DESWEN

2

DOUBLES 1

Many words in English are made of 2 words. Look at the pictures and put the word from list A with the correct word from list B.

For example: ASH + TRAY = ASHTRAY
MATCH + BOX = MATCHBOX

A	B
ASH	ACHE
MATCH	CHILD
UP	CLUB
GRAND	TRAY
BOOK	MAN
TAPE	SHOP
NIGHT-	STAIRS
DOOR	MAN
POST	RECORDER
HEAD	BOX
BUSINESS	STEP

LBERT'S

Can you name these sports and write them in the correct column?

1.

2.

3.

4.

5.

6.

Individual usually done alone	Needs 2 or 4 people	Needs a team
	For example: 1. squash	

7.

8.

9.

10.

11.

12.

13.

14.

15.

16.

17.

18.

squash skiing boxing table tennis rugby tennis badminton
basketball running hockey baseball water-skiing snooker
fishing shooting diving ice skating cricket

Station Signs

All these signs can be seen at railway stations.
Can you find the word or words to explain these signs?

1.

2.

3.

4.

For example: 1. luggage lockers

15.

5.

Number		
1.	luggage	cafeteria
	information	lockers
	buffet	property
	lost	room
	facilities	water
	meeting	telephone
	waiting	and washroom
	luggage	for the
	public	handicapped
	left	rental
	car	smokers
	toilets	trolleys
	non-	point
	drinking	luggage

14.

6.

13.

7.

12.

11.

10.

9.

8.
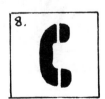

Word Families 1

Here are 24 words. Can you put them into 6 different subject groups?

saucer pair frost dozen pot wound minister party member
directory call box thunderstorm disease socialist fever operator
billion dish injury lightning communist couple pan gale dial

For example:
saucer

_____ _____ _____

_____ _____ _____

_____ _____ _____

_____ _____ _____

WAITING ROOM

_____ _____ _____

_____ _____ _____

_____ _____ _____

_____ _____ _____

Map Reading

Look at the map. What do the symbols represent?
Complete the key.

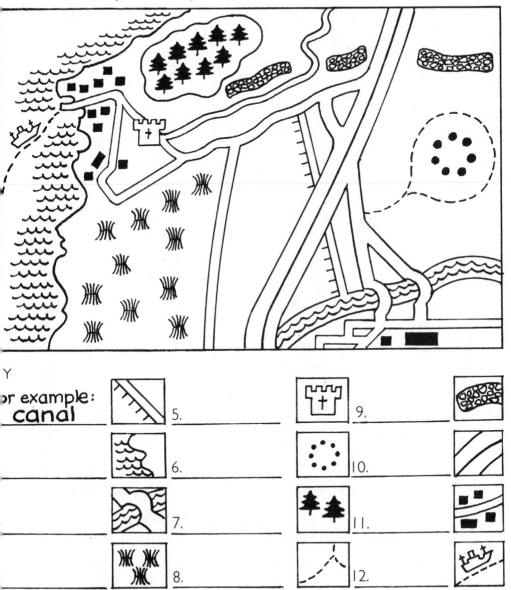

Y

or example:
canal

5. ____

6. ____

7. ____

8. ____

9. ____

10. ____

11. ____

12. ____

canal farmland motorway footpath coast old wall
ferry stone circle village forest bridge castle

The Application Form

Jane Anderson has filled in this application for a new job.
You have her answers. Can you finish the form?

APPLICATION FORM

Please type or write clearly.

For Example
1. *FAMILY NAME* ...Anderson........   2. _____   Ms....

3. _____   Jane Irene......   York...

4. _____   30ᵗʰ July 1961...   5. _____   None..

6. _____   Single.............   7. _____

      27 Glenhill Gardens, Richmond......

8. _____   Sussex......   9. _____   584-29-01

      York Girls' School ...'72-79........

10. _____

      Raydon College of Art '79-'83.....

11. _____   Diploma in Art and Design (Dip AD)'83

      Art and Craft Summer School (Assistant

12. _____   Teacher) Spain '83+'84.........

      Art Department J.Y.C. magazine

13. _____   £8,500 P.A.....

14. _____   French and Spanish, German (a little)

15. _____

16. _____   Yes.........

      Photography, Astronomy, Mountain

17. _____   Climbing..........

      Ignacio Ibañez.   S. Warlock.......

18. _____   430 5:4 Calle Muñoz   Art Director....

      Tarragona, Spain..   22 Bedhill Place.

      from January 1ˢᵗ '86:............

19. _____   Nov. 15ᵗʰ '85.   21 _____

20. _____   *Jane Anderson*

Family name   Interests   Tel. no.   Education: schools attended   Signature
Marital status   Languages spoken   Names and addresses of 2 referees
First names   Place of birth   Education: university/college   Mr/Mrs/Miss/Ms
Date available   Date   Present address   Children   Driving licence
Present position   Date of birth   Present salary   Previous experience

A Picnic in the Country

Look at this busy scene in the country. What are people doing?
Answer with TRUE or FALSE.

For example:	True	False
1. Someone's reading.	X	
2. Someone's swimming.		X
3. Someone's driving.		
4. Someone's climbing.		
5. Someone's drinking.		
6. Someone's riding.		
7. Someone's resting.		
8. Someone's fighting.		
9. Someone's jumping.		
10. Someone's sewing.		

	True	False
11. Someone's crying.		
12. Someone's shaving.		
13. Someone's hurrying.		
14. Someone's laughing.		
15. Someone's hiding.		
16. Someone's standing.		
17. Someone's leaving.		
18. Someone's shooting.		
19. Someone's watching.		
20. Someone's running.		

ABBREVIATIONS 1

Do you understand these abbreviations? Write them out in full

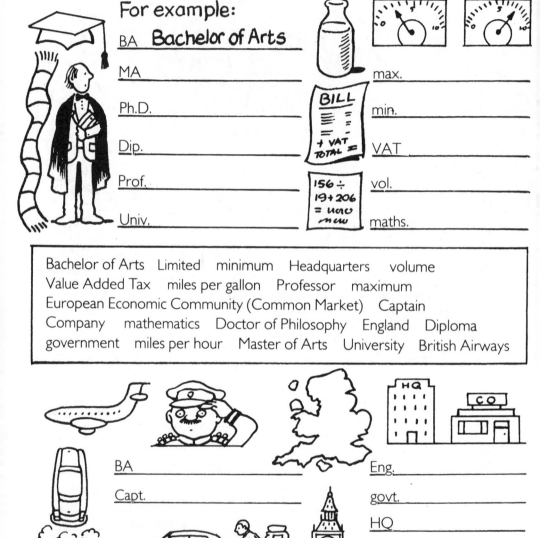

For example:

BA **Bachelor of Arts**

MA _____

Ph.D. _____

Dip. _____

Prof. _____

Univ. _____

max. _____

min. _____

VAT _____

vol. _____

maths. _____

Bachelor of Arts   Limited   minimum   Headquarters   volume
Value Added Tax   miles per gallon   Professor   maximum
European Economic Community (Common Market)   Captain
Company   mathematics   Doctor of Philosophy   England   Diploma
government   miles per hour   Master of Arts   University   British Airways

---

BA _____

Capt. _____

m.p.h. _____

m.p.g. _____

Eng. _____

govt. _____

HQ _____

Ltd. _____

Co. _____

EEC _____

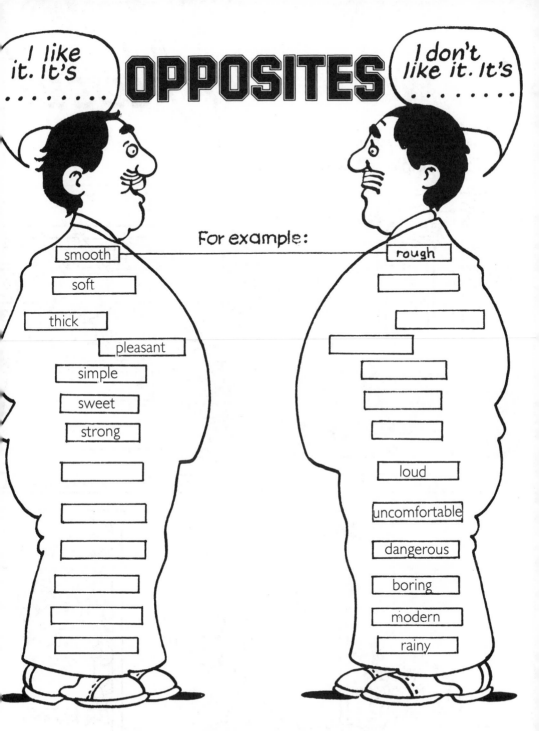

rough   interesting   hard   thin   weak   bitter   fine
difficult   unpleasant   safe   comfortable   soft   antique

Hotel

Can you put each sign in its correct place?

For example: 1. Ring for service

Ring for service   Porter   Lounge   Please do not disturb   Swimming pool   Tour

Signs

Messages for guests   Manager   Roof garden   Check in here   Laundry   Luggage

CROSSWORD 1

All the answers are connected with **position**. Use the rabbit to help you.

Across: ➡

Down: ⬇

14

oo and ee

Look at this picture.
Can you find 11 words with double o '00' and 8 with double e 'EE'?

For example: b<u>oo</u>ts, sl<u>ee</u>ves

MASCULINE and FEMININE

What is the feminine of these words?

For example:

1. male _____female_____

2. actor _____

3. uncle _____

4. bull _____

5. steward _____

6. king _____

7. hero _____

And what is the masculine of these words?

For example:

8. lioness _____lion_____

9. Englishwoman _____

10. mistress _____

11. wife _____

12. waitress _____

13. niece _____

14. lady _____

Clothes

Can you name and describe the clothes these people are wearing?
Put the correct word from list A with the correct description from list B.

For example:
1. A large
handkerchief

A	B
1. handkerchief	fur
2. T-shirt	patterned
3. bra	plastic
4. sweater	dark
5. raincoat	short-sleeved
6. tie	collarless
7. belt	silk
8. shirt	plain
9. suit	child's
10. gloves	large

DRIN   BURGER   COFFEE

17

Odd One Out 1

Look at these groups of words.
Which word does not fit?

For example:

1. SMILE
KISS
TASTE
~~LISTEN~~

2. STADIUM
GROUND
FIELD
TEAM

3. STRING
SOAP
TOWEL
RAZOR

4. PIG
HORSE
SHEEP
BEEF

5. MEANING
INCORRECT
MISTAKE
WRONG

6. CELLAR
LAVATORY
ROOF
STAIRS

In this word square there are 15 hidden words, all connected with money matters. The words are horizontal ⬭, vertical ⬭, or diagonal ⬭ .

For example:

A	C	B	P	R	I	C	E	C	T
T	O	U	D	R	E	Z	Y	V	A
R	I	D	R	C	O	S	T	E	X
E	N	P	F	R	G	F	H	Q	A
C	H	E	Q	U	E	B	I	L	L
E	W	U	W	I	E	N	L	T	X
I	A	C	A	S	H	A	C	F	Y
P	G	J	S	A	L	A	R	Y	M
T	E	D	I	S	C	O	U	N	T

19

AT THE THEATRE

Can you find your way in an English theatre?

For example:
1. cloakroom.

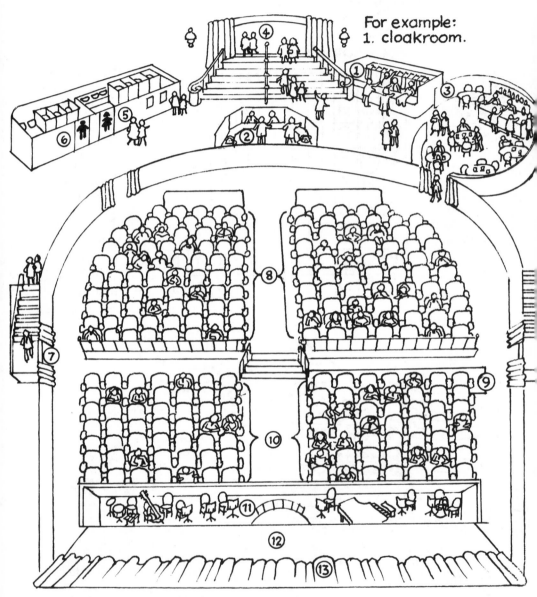

cloakroom   row   orchestra   stage   emergency exit   bar   entrance
front seats   ladies   back seats   gents   booking office   curtain

What Would You Say?

Look at these everyday situations. Do you know what to say?

For example: 1. What's the matter?

What's the matter?   Cheerio.   Good Luck.   That's a pity.   Excuse me.
Mind out!   May I introduce you to Peter Brown?   What a surprise!
Sorry.   Cheers.   No thank you.   How do you do?

ABBREVIATIONS 2

Can you fill in the correct abbreviations?

For example:

Information

Opposite

Please reply

In other words (that is)

Christmas

January

Member of Parliament

Post Office

Long-playing (record)

President

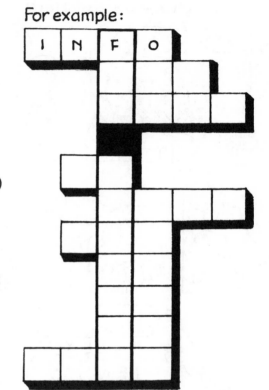

In the centre box you now have 2 words.
Do you know the abbreviation for these 2 words?

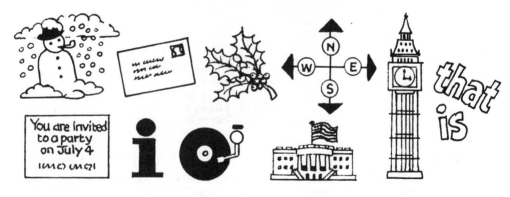

EMERGENCY

Help! These 8 people have problems. What services do they need?
Can you find the solutions in the box?

vet   optician   police   dry cleaner   mechanic
ambulance   fire service   electrician

CHRISTMAS

Look at Susan's Christmas presents. Who are they for?
Put the correct names on her list.

Christmas list
spade   - Bill
teddy bear
fridge
shirt
shoes
pack of cards
record
purse
suitcase
hammer
cupboard
football
Christmas cake

SHOPPING

Susan bought all her Christmas presents in one big shop. Which departments did she go to?

SUPER SHOP

DEPARTMENTS

Children's

Do-it-Yourself

Food

Footwear

Furniture

Games

Gardening

Kitchen

Luggage

Men's

Music

Sports

Women's Leather Goods

teddy bear

CROSSWORD 2

All the answers are connected with **punctuation** and **writing**.

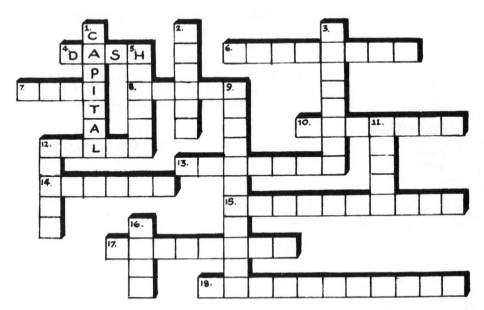

ACROSS ➡

4. ▬

6. ❝ ❞ (_____ commas)

7. ⦂ (_____ colon)

8. ●●●

10. LATEST ⬅

12. ⦂

13. ~~the~~ *the*

14. ├─┤

15. it'ʼs

17. ? (_____ mark)

18. the

DOWN ⬇

1. English (_____ letter)

2. 〰〰〰〰

3. ( )

5. ▬ week-end

9. ! (_____ mark)

11. ❞ (2 tins of beans ʼʼ ʼʼ ʼʼ carrots)

12. ❜

16. ● (_____ stop)

26

PREPOSITIONS 1

Here are 10 very common expressions with **at**. Do you know them all?

For example: 1. at university

university   sea   full speed   home   work
school   war   peace   church   breakfast

Person or Thing?

Here are 20 words which end in **-er**.
Which of them is a person and which is a thing?
Make 2 lists.

For example:

Person	Thing
driver	lighter

LIGHTER
DRIVER
SAUCER
PASSENGER
PHOTOGRAPHER

SCOOTER
FOREIGNER
LABOURER
TYPEWRITER
MEMBER

COOKER
SHOWER
PLAYER
EMPLOYER
TRAVELLER

GROCER
INTERVIEWER
NOTEPAPER
DANCER
FARMER

NATIONALITIES

In this word square there are 12 hidden words. They are all different nationalities.

The words are horizontal ⬭ vertical ⬯ or diagonal ⬭.
The hats will help you.

or example: chinese

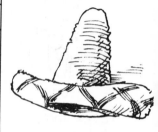

S	C	O	T	T	I	S	H	V	S
A	D	F	P	F	R	E	N	C	H
U	M	U	V	O	S	G	T	L	B
S	Z	E	T	M	H	Y	V	U	R
T	W	N	R	C	O	P	P	S	I
R	A	Q	X	I	H	T	Y	C	T
I	H	Y	Z	R	C	I	B	H	I
A	M	E	X	I	C	A	N	I	S
N	E	I	K	E	D	N	N	N	H
I	N	D	I	A	N	B	P	E	M
G	F	A	S	P	A	N	I	S	H
R	U	S	S	I	A	N	O	E	N

29

Word Families 2

Can you put these words into 5 different subject groups?
There are 4 words in each.

Atlantic   buffet   North Sea   classical   Africa   water   Pacific
rock   canteen   gas   snack bar   pop   Australasia   pub   jazz
Europe   phone   Mediterranean   Asia   electricity

1.

For example:
Atlantic
_____
_____
_____

2.

_____
_____
_____

3.

_____
_____
_____

4.

_____
_____
_____
_____

5.

_____
_____
_____

Help in the Home

Mrs. Brown is talking to her au pair girl Marie and asking her to do different things in the house.

Look at the pictures and tell Marie what to do.

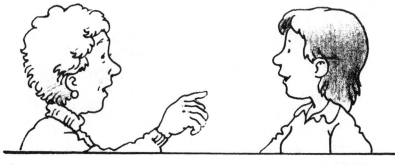

For example:
1. Please fill the kettle

fill   polish   paint   fasten   lay   cook   repair
post   wrap   carry   feed   clean   change

THIEVES

Look at the pictures and answer the questions.

What did the thieves damage?
For example:

1. hedge _____ drainpipe_____

What did the thieves use?

2. _____ _____

_____ _____

hedge   drainpipe   picture   washing line   torch   blood
jewellery   window   dustbin   television aerial   clock
ladder   footprints   handbag   bricks   scarf

What did the thieves find?

3. _____ _____

_____ _____

What did the detective find?

4. _____ _____

_____ _____

Make a Choice

Look carefully at the pictures and choose the correct answers.

For example:

1. Is it (a) a bottle of wine
   or (b) a wine bottle?

☒

2. Is it (a) the boy's dog
   or (b) the boys' dog?

3. It is (a) a cup of coffee
   or (b) a coffee cup?

4. Is it (a) a matchbox
   or (b) a box of matches?

5. Are they (a) the farmer's son's cows
   or (b) the farmer's sons' cows?

6. Is it (a) a picture of Susan
   or (b) a picture by Susan?

7. Is it (a) a sculpture of a woman
   or (b) a sculpture by a woman?

8. Is it (a) Agatha Christie's book
   or (b) a book by Agatha Christie?

9. Is she (a) the baby's mother
   or (b) the babies' mother?

10. Is it (a) a wine glass
    or (b) a glass of wine?

Shopping Centre

To buy everything on this shopping list, you must go to 13 different shops. Show the way you would go, following the numbers on the list.

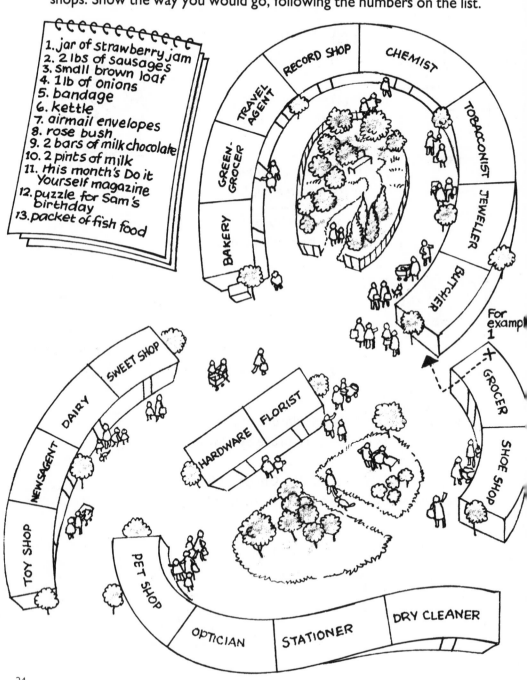

1. jar of strawberry jam
2. 2 lbs of sausages
3. small brown loaf
4. 1 lb of onions
5. bandage
6. kettle
7. airmail envelopes
8. rose bush
9. 2 bars of milk chocolate
10. 2 pints of milk
11. this month's Do it Yourself magazine
12. puzzle for Sam's birthday
13. packet of fish food

DOUBLES 2

Many words in English are made of two parts.
Put the word from list A with the correct word from list B.

For example: CENTRAL + HEATING = CENTRAL HEATING

A	B
CENTRAL	PARK
RECORD-	MINISTER
PRIME	BOX
INFORMATION	STATION
SNACK	MACHINE
DRIVING	PLAYER
BUS	ROADS
CROSS	HEATING
LETTER	DESK
CAR	LICENCE
WASHING	STOP
PETROL	BAR

GENERAL ELECTION RESULTS

SNACKS
Sandwiches · Hot drinks · Cold drinks

ER

Thank You

How would you say **thank you** in these situations?

For example:

visit   call   lift   help   present   party   loan   hospitality   meal   advice

Work for us!

Look at these job advertisements.
Can you fill in the missing words?

HEAD OF LANGUAGES IN PRIVATE SCHOOL
FULL _Responsibility_
HIGH
LONG
GENEROUS

For example:

CAR FACTORY NEEDS WORKERS
FRIENDLY
FREE
SHORT
SELF-SERVICE

CANTEEN

WANTED SECRETARY FOR TRAVEL AGENT
PLEASANT
ELECTRIC
MODERN
TRAVEL

responsibility
canteen
holidays
office
boss
colleagues
hours
salary
typewriter
pension
transport
opportunities

Odd One Out 2

Look at these groups of words. Find the words which do not fit.

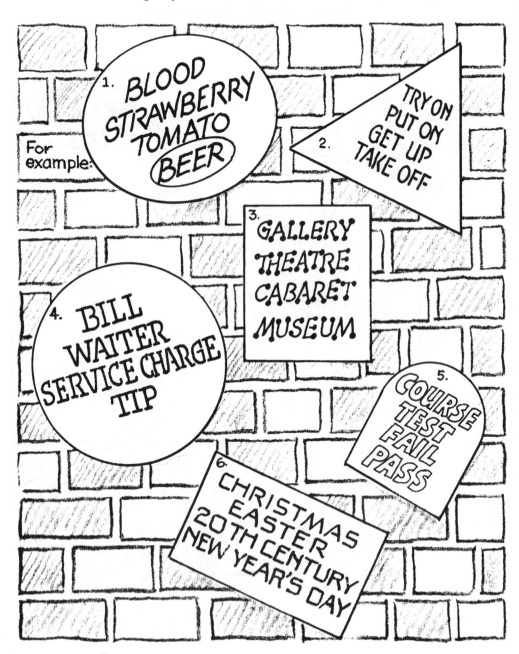

For example:

1. BLOOD
STRAWBERRY
TOMATO
(BEER)

2. TRY ON
PUT ON
GET UP
TAKE OFF

3. GALLERY
THEATRE
CABARET
MUSEUM

4. BILL
WAITER
SERVICE CHARGE
TIP

5. COURSE
TEST
FAIL
PASS

6. CHRISTMAS
EASTER
20TH CENTURY
NEW YEAR'S DAY

PREPOSITIONS 2

Here are 12 common expressions with **in**. Can you find them all?

For example: **1.** in love

love   prison   turn   half   tears   a hurry   bed
pieces   trouble   ink   town   danger

Travel Quiz

All these words are connected with **holidays**.
Can you choose the correct explanation?

For example:

1. To **register** is
a   to pay your bill in a hotel   ☐
b   to record your name in a hotel   ☒
c   to leave your luggage in a hotel   ☐
d   to have a meal in a hotel   ☐

2. A **view** is
a   something you taste   ☐
b   something you wear   ☐
c   something you see   ☐
d   something you hear   ☐

3. A **receipt** is
a   kind of visa   ☐
b   a record of payment   ☐
c   an insurance document   ☐
d   a single ticket   ☐

4. A **hotel guest** is
a   a person who works in a hotel   ☐
b   a person who is waiting to get a room   ☐
c   a person who is staying at the hotel   ☐
d   a person who recommends hotels   ☐

5. A **caravan** is
a   used to sit on   ☐
b   used to lie on   ☐
c   used to live in   ☐
d   used to sail with   ☐

6. A **message** is
a   a snack   ☐
b   a friend   ☐
c   a piece of news   ☐
d   a parcel   ☐

7. A **flight** is
a   a trip by air   ☐
b   a trip by sea   ☐
c   a trip by train   ☐
d   a trip by car   ☐

8. **Abroad** is
a   outside your own country   ☐
b   in your country   ☐
c   when you are on holiday   ☐
d   in Europe   ☐

9. A **youth hostel** is
a   a kind of reduction for young people   ☐
b   a kind of hotel   ☐
c   a kind of exhibition   ☐
d   a kind of children's room   ☐

10. A **fare** is
a   an amusement park   ☐
b   a place to put your luggage   ☐
c   an extra charge on a bill   ☐
d   the price of a journey   ☐

11. **Welcome** is
a   a greeting   ☐
b   a food   ☐
c   a class of hotel   ☐
d   a warning   ☐

12. A **frontier** is
a   a foreign currency   ☐
b   a foreign country   ☐
c   between two countries   ☐
d   an immigration form   ☐

WHERE DOES IT GO?

Identify the objects in A and B. Each object from A can go into one of the objects in B. Can you put them together?

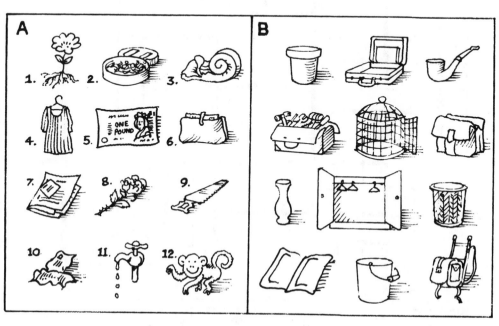

plant   document   rubbish
evening dress   rose   water
sleeping bag   monkey   saw
pound note   tobacco   purse

flower pot   wallet   cage
rucksack   wastepaper basket
vase   pipe   wardrobe   tool box
handbag   briefcase   bucket

For example:

1. A plant goes in a flower pot

2. Tobacco

3.

4.

5.

6.

7.

8.

9.

10.

11.

12.

CROSSWORD 3

All the answers are connected with **entertainment**.

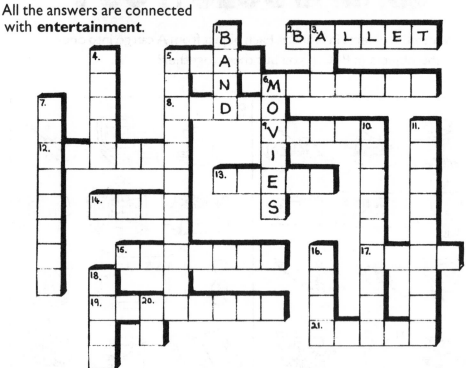

ACROSS →

DOWN ↓

Prefixes & Suffixes

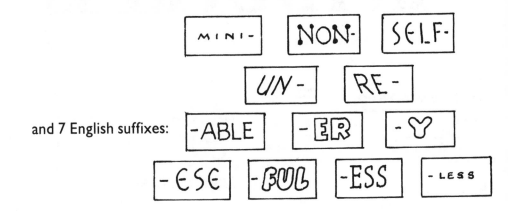

and 7 English suffixes:

Can you put them in the correct place?

For example: **useless**

1. USE
2. LION
3. SERVICE
4. SPOON
5. JAPAN
6. IRON
7. SKIRT
8. BUILD
9. CHANGE
10. LEAD
11. HAIR
12. USUAL

IN THE PRESS

All these items are from pages of a newspaper. Can you fill in the Contents List?

page 2

WHERE GRADUATES GO

	Permanent UK work %	Further study %
Art & Design	41.5	9.0
Biological Sciences	34.6	27.5
Business Management	75.8	3.5
Chemistry	37.6	34.2

page 14

Sagittarius

page 10

THAILAND 50 miles

Aranyaprathet

Bangkok

GULF OF THAILAND

page 4

OPERA AND BALLET

ROYAL OPERA HOUSE COVENT GARDEN. Resv.', 01-240 1066/1911 Access, Visa, Diners Club. 5. Standby info. 01-836 6903. 65 amphi seats available from 10 am on the day. Tickets Opera £2.00-£34.00 Ballet £1.00-£20.00.

page 9

Sir, Today I saw my bank manager with a shovel in his hands. He was outside the bank, alone, chipping frozen snow from the pavement. A sign of the times?

Yours truly,

page 7

BBC 1 Wales: 8.30-9.00am Rugby Union: Try, try again. 5.15-5.20pm Sports News Wales. 12.30-12.35am News. Scotland: 12.15-5.05pm Grandstand. Including Rugby Union

page 4

CLARE. On February 21st at King's College Hospital to Jane (nee Hogan) And Anthony, a son Sebastian, a brother for Rachel, Simon, Eleanor, Peter, Sophie and Justine.

page 13

TENNIS

ROSENHEIM, West Germany: Winter circuit tournament, quarter-finals: H-D Beutel (WG) bt A Zveran (USSR), 6-3, 6-7, 7-5; S Birner (Cz) bt C Zipf (WG), 6-2, 6-3; F Segarceanu (Rom) bt W Popp (WG), 6-2, 3-6, 6-3; P Carlsson (Swe) bt U Fischer (WG), 6-3, 7-6.

page 12

LONDON COMMODITY PRICES

Rubber in £'s per tonne; Coffee, cocoa, sugar in pounds per metric ton; Gas-oil in US $ per metric tonne. G W Joynson and Co report

COCOA

Mar	2118-15
May	2135-34
Jly	2119-16
Sep	2104-03

page 6

WINTER SPORTS

SKI WHIZZ

NO 1 FOR CHALET FUN! Superb resorts Inclusive prices!

March 16 £209	March 30 £229
March 23 £259	April 6 £219
April 13 £164	

FILL A CHALET – YOU GO FREE!

Contents

	Page
For example:	
Careers Information	2
	4
	4
	5
	6
	7
	9
	10
	12
	12
	13
	14

page 5

Solution of Puzzle No 16,657

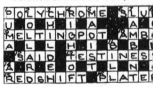

page 12

PINE SALE ENDS SUNDAY

THE LARGEST STOCK OF FINEST QUALITY SOLID PINE FURNITURE AT THE VERY KEENEST PRICES IN YOUR AREA

Goldpine Furniture

Nationwide deliveries. Write or phone for lists

Careers Information Travel & Holidays Readers' Letters Foreign News
Horoscopes Births, Marriages & Deaths Entertainments Guide
Advertisements TV & Radio Sport Crossword Business

BOOKS

Here are 12 students working in the college library.
Look carefully at the titles of the books they are reading.
What subjects are the students studying?

For example: 1. He is studying poetry

poetry   jazz appreciation   psychology   antiques   first aid
the modern novel   keep fit   translation   dressmaking
wine-making   banking   computer science.

The Word Snake

There are 32 words in this snake. They are all connected up and are associated with **transport** and **movement**.
Can you find them?

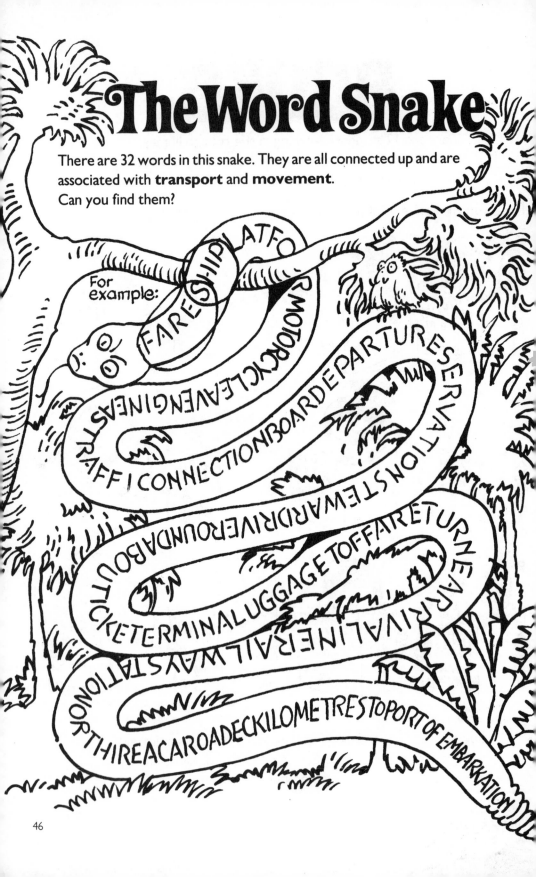

For example:

FARESHIPLATFORMOTORCYCLEAVENGINESTRAFFICONNECTIONBOARDEPARTURESERVATIONSTEWARDRIVEROUNDABOUTICKETERMINALUGGAGETOFFARETURNEARRIVALRAILWAYSTATIONORTHIREACAROADECKILOMETRESTOPORTOFEMBARKATION

Answers

Quick Service Page 1

Order No. 1: roast pork and peas
Order No. 2: ham salad and bread roll
Order No. 3: spaghetti with tomato sauce
Order No. 4: grilled lamb, mushrooms and peas
Order No. 5: strawberries and cream
Order No. 6: boiled beef, carrots and cabbage
Order No. 7: fried bacon and sausages
Order No. 8: vanilla ice-cream and pears

Around the World
Page 2

1. Norway   2. Wales   3. Argentina
4. Cyprus   5. Denmark   6. Portugal
7. Thailand   8. Panama   9. New Zealand
10. Turkey   11. United States   12. Sweden

Doubles 1 Page 3

ashtray, matchbox, upstairs, grandchild,
bookshop, tape recorder, night-club,
doorstep, postman, headache, businessman

Sports Page 4

Individuals: 4. waterskiing   5. fishing
  7. running   8. ice-skating   13. shooting
  17. skiing   18. diving

2 or more people: 1. squash   2. table tennis
  6. snooker   10. tennis   12. boxing
  16. badminton

Teams: 3. baseball   9. rugby   11. cricket
  14. basketball   15. hockey

Station Signs Page 5

1. luggage locker
2. facilities for the handicapped
3. left luggage
4. luggage trolleys
5. information
6. car rental
7. non-smokers
8. public telephone
9. lost property
10. toilets and washroom
11. cafeteria
12. buffet
13. drinking water
14. meeting point
15. waiting room

Word Families 1 Page 6

1. saucer, pot, dish, pan
2. socialist, party member, minister, communist
3. operator, directory, dial, call box
4. wound, injury, disease, fever
5. gale, thunderstorm, lightning, frost
6. pair, couple, billion, dozen

Map Reading Page 7

1. canal   7. forest

2. coast   8. footpath

3. bridge   9. old wall

4. farmland   10. motorway

5. castle   11. village

6. stone circle   12. ferry

47

The Application Form Page 8

1. Family name 2. Mr/Mrs/Miss/Ms 3. First name 4. Date of birth 5. Place of birth 6. Marital status 7. Children 8. Present address 9. Tel. no. 10. Education: schools attended 11. Education: university/ college 12. Previous experience 13. Present position 14. Present salary 15. Languages spoken 16. Driving licence 17. Interests 18. Names and addresses of 2 referees 19. Date available 20. Date 21. Signature

A Picnic in the Country Page 9

	True	False
1. Someone's reading.	X	
2. Someone's swimming.		X
3. Someone's driving.		X
4. Someone's climbing.	X	
5. Someone's drinking.		X
6. Someone's riding.		X
7. Someone's resting.	X	
8. Someone's fighting.	X	
9. Someone's jumping.	X	
10. Someone's sewing.	X	
11. Someone's crying.	X	
12. Someone's shaving.		X
13. Someone's hurrying.		X
14. Someone's laughing.		X
15. Someone's hiding.	X	
16. Someone's standing.	X	
17. Someone's leaving.		X
18. Someone's shooting.		X
19. Someone's watching.	X	
20. Someone's running.		X

Abbreviations 1

Page 10

BA – Bachelor of Arts MA – Master of Arts Ph.D. – Doctor of Philosophy Dip.– Diploma Prof. – Professor Univ. – university max. – maximum min.– minimum VAT – value added tax vol. – volume maths.– mathematics BA – British Airways Capt. – Captain m.p.h. – miles per hour m.p.g. – miles per gallon Eng. – England govt. – government HQ – Headquarters Ltd.– Limited Co. – Company EEC – European Economic Community (Common Market).

Opposites Page 11

smooth – rough soft – hard thick – thin; pleasant – unpleasant simple – difficult sweet – bitter strong – weak soft – loud: comfortable – uncomfortable safe – dangerous interesting – boring antique – modern, fine – rainy

Hotel Signs Page 12

1. Ring for service 2. Messages for guests 3. Check in here 4. Luggage 5. Laundry 6. Porter 7. Lounge, 8. Tours 9. Roof garden 10. Manager 11. Please do not disturb 12. Swimming pool

Crossword 1 Page 14

OO and EE Page 15

OO: boot, wool, roof, cooker, root, balloon, pool, moon, scooter, door, floor
EE: queen, feet, tree, wheel, sheep, fifteen, sleeve, knee

Masculine & Feminine Page 16

Feminine: 1. female   2. actress   3. aunt
   4. cow   5. stewardess   6. queen
   7. heroine
Masculine: 8. lion   9. Englishman
   10. master   11. husband   12. waiter
   13. nephew   14. gentleman

Clothes Page 17

1. a large handkerchief
2. a plain T-shirt
3. a patterned bra
4. a short-sleeved sweater
5. a child's raincoat
6. a silk tie
7. a plastic belt
8. a collarless shirt
9. a dark suit
10. fur gloves

Odd One Out 1 Page 18

1. listen.   2. team.   3. string.   4. beef
5. meaning   6. roof.

Money Page 19

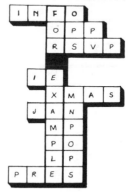

price   tax   salary
cheque   tip   receipt
cash   earn   wage
discount   cost   profit
coin   bill   currency

At the Theatre Page 20

1. cloakroom   2. booking office   3. bar
4. entrance   5. ladies   6. gents
7. emergency exit   8. back seats   9. row
10. front seats   11. orchestra   12. stage
13. curtain

What would you Say? Page 21

1. What's the matter?
2. Sorry.
3. How do you do?
4. Excuse me.
5. No thank you.
6. Good Luck.
7. That's a pity.
8. Cheers.
9. Mind out!
10. What a surprise!
11. May I introduce you to Peter Brown.
12. Cheerio.

Abbreviations 2 Page 22

I	N	F	O		
		O	P	P	
		R	S	V	P
	I	E			
		X	M	A	S
	J	A	N		
		M	P		
		P	O		
		L	P		
	P	R	E	S	

For Example = e.g.

Emergency Page 23

1. A vet,   2. E police,   3. H ambulance,
4. C fire service,   5. F electrician,
6. B dry cleaner,   7. D mechanic,
8. G optician.

Christmas Shopping <small>Page 24</small>

Christmas list: spade – Bill   teddy bear – Liz
fridge – Sue   shirt – Jim   shoes – Mary
pack of cards – Dick   record – Mike
purse – Kate   suitcase – Joe
hammer – Bob   cupboard – Ann
football – Tom   Christmas cake – Jane

Super Shop departments: Children's
– teddy bear   Do-it-Yourself – hammer
Food – Christmas cake   Footwear – shoes
Furniture – cupboard   Games – pack of cards
Gardening – spade   Kitchen – fridge
Luggage – suitcase   Men's – shirt
Music – record   Sports – football
Women's Leather Goods – purse

Crossword 2 <small>Page 26</small>

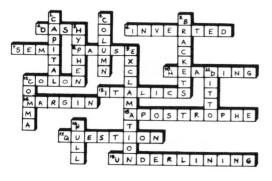

Prepositions 1 <small>Page 27</small>

1. at university   2. at home   3. at peace
4. at war   5. at work   6. at breakfast
7. at church   8. at full speed   9. at school
10. at sea

Person or Thing? <small>Page 28</small>

Person: driver, passenger, photographer,
   player, employer, traveller, foreigner,
   labourer, member, grocer, interviewer,
   dancer, farmer.
Thing: lighter, saucer, cooker, shower,
   scooter, typewriter, notepaper.

Nationalities <small>Page 29</small>

S	C	O	T	T	I	S	H	V	S
A	D	F	P	F	R	E	N	C	H
U	M	U	V	O	S	G	T	L	B
S	Z	E	T	M	H	Y	V	U	R
T	W	N	R	C	O	P	P	S	I
R	A	Q	X	I	H	T	Y	C	T
I	H	Y	Z	R	C	I	B	H	I
A	M	E	X	I	C	A	N	I	S
N	E	I	K	E	D	N	N	N	H
I	N	D	I	A	N	B	P	E	M
G	F	A	S	P	A	N	I	S	H
R	U	S	S	I	A	N	O	E	N

Chinese	Indian	Egyptian
British	Dutch	Mexican
Russian	French	Scottish
American	Austrian	Spanish

Word Families 2 <small>Page 30</small>

1. Atlantic, Mediterranean, Pacific, North Sea
2. electricity, phone, water, gas
3. rock, classical, pop, jazz
4. buffet, snack bar, canteen, pub
5. Australasia, Africa, Europe, Asia

Help in the Home
<small>Page 31</small>

1. Please fill the kettle.
2. Please feed the dog.
3. Please repair the vase.
4. Please lay the table.

5. Please fasten the dress.
6. Please polish the desk.
7. Please change the sheets.
8. Please post the letter.
9. Please cook the sausages.
10. Please carry the bag.
11. Please paint the cupboard.
12. Please wrap the book.
13. Please clean the carpet.

Thieves Page 32

1. hedge, drainpipe, television aerial, window
2. dustbin, bricks, washing line, ladder
3. clock, handbag, picture, jewellery
4. torch, footprints, blood, scarf

Make a Choice Page 33

1.b 2.b 3.a 4.b 5.a 6.b 7.a 8.b
9.b 10.a

Shopping Centre

Page 34

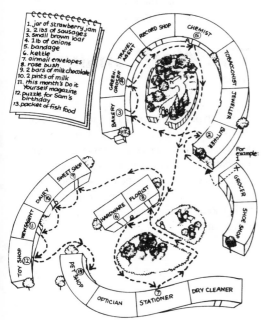

Doubles 2 Page 35

central heating, record-player, Prime Minister, information desk, snack bar, driving licence, bus stop, crossroads, letter box, car park, washing machine, petrol station.

Thank you Page 36

1. Thank you for the visit.
2. Thank you for the present.
3. Thank you for the meal.
4. Thank you for the help.
5. Thank you for the call.
6. Thank you for the advice.
7. Thank you for the lift.
8. Thank you for the party.
9. Thank you for the loan.
10. Thank you for the hospitality.

Work for Us Page 37

Head of Languages in private school: full responsibility, high salary, long holidays, generous pension.

Car factory needs workers: friendly colleagues, free transport, short hours, self-service canteen.

Private secretary for travel agent: pleasant boss, electric typewriter, modern office, travel opportunities.

Odd One Out 2 Page 38

1. beer 2. get up 3. cabaret 4. waiter
5. course 6. 20th century

Prepositions 2 Page 39

1. in love 2. in bed 3. in tears 4. in ink
5. in danger 6. in half 7. in town
8. in pieces 9. in prison 10. in a hurry
11. in trouble 12. in turn

Travel Quiz Page 40

1.b 2.c 3.b 4.c 5.c 6.c 7.a 8.a
9.b 10.d 11.a 12.c

Where does it go?

Page 41

1. A plant goes in a flower pot.
2. Tobacco goes in a pipe.
3. A sleeping bag goes in a rucksack.
4. An evening dress goes in a wardrobe.
5. A pound note goes in a wallet.
6. A purse goes in a handbag.
7. A document goes in a brief case.
8. A rose goes in a vase.
9. A saw goes in a tool box.
10. Rubbish goes in a wastepaper basket.
11. Water goes in a bucket.
12. A monkey goes in a cage.

Crossword 3 Page 42

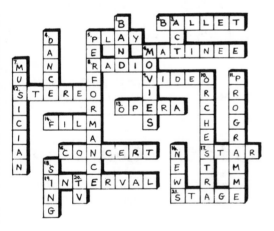

Prefixes & Suffixes

Page 43

1. useless   2. lioness   3. self-service
4. spoonful   5. Japanese   6. non-iron
7. mini-skirt   8. rebuild   9. changeable
10. leader   11. hairy   12. unusual

In the Press Page 44

Contents	Page
Careers Information	2
Entertainments Guide	4
Births, Marriages & Deaths	4
Travel & Holidays	6
TV & Radio	7
Readers' Letters	9
Foreign News	10
Business	12
Advertisements	12
Sport	13
Horoscopes	14

Books Page 45

1. He is studying poetry.
2. He is studying wine-making.
3. She is studying psychology.
4. He is studying computer science.
5. She is studying antiques.
6. He is studying jazz appreciation.
7. She is studying keep fit.
8. She is studying dressmaking.
9. He is studying the modern novel.
10. She is studying translation.
11. He is studying first aid.
12. She is studying banking.

The Word Snake

Page 46

fares, ship, platform, motorcycle, leave, engine, east, traffic, connection, on board departure, reservations, steward, driver, roundabout, ticket, terminal, luggage, get off, far, return, near, arrival, liner, railway station, north, hire a car, road, deck, kilometres, stop, port of embarkation

WORD LIST

A

abbreviation 10, 22
above 14
abroad 40
across 14
act 42
actor 16
actress 16
address 8
advertisements 37, 44
advice 36
aerial 32
Africa 30
against 14
Agatha Christie 33
air 40
airmail 34
all 4, 14, 45
alone 4
ambulance 23
American 29
among 14
amusement 40
Ann 25
answer 8, 9, 14
antique 11, 45
application 8
apostrophe 26
appreciation 45
Argentina 2
around 2
arrival 46
art 8
ashtray 3
Asia 30
assistant 8
astronomy 8
Atlantic 30
attended 8
aunt 16
au pair 31
Australasia 30
Austrian 29
available 8

B

baby(ies) 33
Bachelor of Arts (BA) 10
back 20
bacon 1
badminton 4
bag 31
baker 34
ballet 42
balloon 15
band 42
bandage 34
banking 45
bar (cafe) 20
bar (chocolate) 34
baseball 4
basement 18
basketball 4
bed (in bed) 39
beef 1, 18
beer 38
behind 14
below 14
belt 17
beside 14
between 14
Bill 24
bill 19, 38, 40
billion 6
birth 8, 44
birthday 34
bitter 11
blood 32, 38
board (on board) 46
Bob 24
body 45
boiled 1
book 31, 33, 45
booking office 20
bookshop 3
boot 15
boring 11
boss 37
bottle 33
box 7, 38
boxing 4
boy 33
bra 17
brackets 26
bread 1
break (broken) 23
breakdown

(brokendown) 23
breakfast (at breakfast) 27
brick 32
briefcase 41
bridge 7
British 29
British Airways (BA) 10
brown 34
bucket 41
buffet 5, 30
bull 16
bush 34
bus stop 35
business 44
businessman 3
busy 9
butcher 34
buy 34

C

cabaret 38
cabbage 1
cafeteria 5
cage 41
cake 24
call 36
call box 6
canal 7
canteen 30, 37
capital (letter) 26
Captain (Capt.) 10
car 5, 23, 37
car park 35
caravan 40
cards 24
carefully 45
career 44
carpet 31
carrot 1
carry 1, 31
cash 19
castle 7
cellar 18
central heating 35
century 38
change 31
changeable 45
charge 40

check in 13
cheerio 21
cheers 21
chemist 34
cheque 17
child 17
children 8, 25, 40
Chinese 29
chocolate
 (milk chocolate) 34
choice 33
choose 40
Christmas
 (Xmas) 22, 24, 38
church (at church) 27
class 40
classical (music) 30
clean 31
clearly 9
climb 9
cloakroom 20
clock 32, 45
clothes 17
coast 7
coffee 33
coin 19
collarless 17
colleague 37
college 8, 45
colon 26
column 4, 26
comfortable 11
comma 26
common 39
Common Market (EEC) 10
communist 6
Company (Co.) 10
computer 45
concert 42
connect 14, 40
connection 46
contents 44
cook 31
cooker 28
correct (correctly) 2, 3, 4
cost 19
country (ies) 2, 9, 40
couple 6

course   38
cow   16, 33
craft   8
cream   1
cricket   4
crossroads   35
crossword   14, 26, 44
cry   9
cupboard   24, 31
currency   19, 40
curtain   20
Cyprus   2

D

dairy   34
damage   32
dance   42
dancer   28
danger (in danger)   39
dangerous   11
dark   17
dash   26
data processing   45
date   8
date of birth   8
death   44
deck   46
Denmark   2
department   8, 25
departure   46
describe   17
description   17
design   8
desk   31
dial   6
Dick   24
dictionary   45
different   1, 6, 18
difficult   11, 29
Diploma (Dip.)   8, 10
director   8
directory   6
dirty   23
discount   19
disease   6
dish (es)   1, 6
dislike   11
disturb (please do not disturb)   12
ditto   26
diving   4
do-it-yourself (DIY)   25, 34

document   40, 41
Doctor of Philosophy (Ph.D.)   10
dog   31, 33
door   15
doorstep   3
double   3, 15, 34
down   14, 23
dozen   6
drainpipe   32
draw (drawn)   2
drawing   7
dress   23, 31
dressmaking   45
drink   5, 9
drinking water   5
drive   9
driver   28, 46
driving licence   8, 35
dry cleaner   23, 34
dustbin   32
Dutch   29

E

earn   19, 45
east   46
Easter   38
education   8
e.g. (for example)   22
electrician   23
electricity   30
emergency   23
emergency exit   20
employer   28
engine   46
England (Eng.)   10
English   45
Englishman   16
Englishwoman   16
entertainments   44
entrance   20
envelopes   34
Europe   30, 40
European Economic Community (EEC)   10
evening dress   41
everyday   21
example   22
exclamation mark   26
excuse me   21
exercises   45
exhibition   40

experience   8
explain   5
explanation   40
expression   39
extra   40

F

facilities   5
factory   37
fail   38
false   9
family (ies)   6, 10
family name   8
fare   40, 46
farmer   28, 33
farmland   7
fasten   31
feed   31
feet   15
female   16
feminine (f)   16
ferry   7
fever   6
field   18
fifteen   15
fight   9
fill (filled)   1, 7, 8
fill in   37
film   42
find   32, 38, 39
fine   11
finish   8
fire   23
fire service   23
first aid   45
first names   8
fish   34
fishing   4
flight   40
floor   15
florist   34
flower pot   41
following   34
food   25, 34, 40
football   24
footpath   7
footprints   32
footwear   25
for example (e.g.)   22
foreign   40, 44
foreigner   28
forest   7

form   8, 40
free   37
French   8, 29, 45
fridge   24
fried   1
friend (friendly)   37, 40
front   20
frontier   40
frost   6
full (at full speed)   27, 37
full-cream   34
full stop   26
fur   17
furniture   25

G

gale   6
gallery   38
games   19, 25
garden   13
gardening   25
gas   30
generous   37
gentleman   16
gents   20
German   8
get   40, 46
get off   38
get up   38
girl   8, 31
give   19
glass (es)   23, 30, 33
gloves   17
golf   4
good luck   21
goods   25
government (govt.)   10
grapes   45
greengrocer   34
greeting   40
grilled   1
grocer   28, 34
ground   18
group   6, 18, 30
guest   13, 40
guide   44

H

hairbrush   41
hairy   43
half (in half)   39

54

ham 1
hammer 24
handbag 32, 41
handkerchief 17
handicapped 5
hard (difficult) 11
hardware 34
hat 29
head (boss) 37
headache 3
heading 26
headquarters (HQ) 10
hedge 32
help (v) 19, 23
help (n) 31, 36
here 45
hero 16
heroine 16
hide 9
high 37
hire (hire a car) 46
hockey 4
holidays 37, 40, 44
home (at home) 27, 31
horoscope 44
horse 18
hospitality 36
hotel 13, 34, 40
hours 37
house 31
How do you do? 21
hurry (in a hurry) 9, 39
husband 16
hyphen 26

I

ice-cream 1
ice-skating 4
identify 29
i.e. (in other words) 22
ill 23
immigration 40
in 14
incorrect 18
Indian 29
individual 4
information (info) 5, 22, 35
injury 6
ink (in ink) 39
inside 12
insurance 40
interest (n) 8

interesting 11
interval 42
interviewer 28
introduce (May I
   introduce you to) 21
inverted commas 26
Irene 8
iron (non-iron) 43
italics 26
items 44

J

jam 34
Jane 8, 25
January (Jan) 22
Japanese 43
jar 34
jazz 30, 45
jewellers 34
jewellery 32
Jim 25
job 8, 37
Joe 24
journey 40
July 8
jump 9

K

Kate 25
keep fit 45
kettle 31, 34
kilometre 46
kind 40
king 16
kiss 18
kitchen 25
knee 15

L

labourer 28
ladder 32
lady (ies) 16, 20
lamb 1
lamp 23
language 8, 37
large 17
laugh 9
lay 31
lb (pound) 34
laundry 13

lavatory 18
leader 43
leather 25
leave 9, 34, 40
left luggage 5
leg 23
letter 31, 44
letter box 35
library 45
lie 40
lift 35
light (music) 30
lighter 28
lightning 6
like 11
Limited (Ltd.) 10
liner 46
lion 16
lioness 16, 43
list 3, 17, 24 ...
listen 18
little 8
live 40
Liz 24
loaf 34
loan 36
locker 5
long 37
long-playing
   record (LP) 22
lost property 5
loud 11
lounge 12
lose (lost) 5
love (in love) 39
LP (long-playing record) 22
luggage 5, 12, 34

M

magazine 8, 17, 34
make 33
male (m) 16
manager 13
map 7
margin 26
Marie 31
marital 8
marriage 44
Mary 25
masculine 16
master 16
Master of Arts (MA) 10

matchbox 3, 33
matches 33
mathematics (maths) 10
matinee 42
matter 21
matters 19
maximum (max.) 10
meal 34, 36
meaning 18
mechanic 23
Mediterranean 30
meeting point 5
member 28
Member of
   Parliament (MP) 22
message 13, 40
Mexican 29
Mike 25
miles per gallon (m.p.g.) 10
miles per hour (m.p.h.) 10
milk 34
mind 45
mind (v) (mind out) 21
minimum (min.) 10
miniskirt 43
minister 6
miss 8
missing 37
mistake 17
mistress 16
modern 11, 37, 45
money 19, 23
monkey 41
month 34
mother 33
motorcycle 46
motorway 7
mountain climbing 8
movies 42
Mr 8
Mrs 8
Mrs Brown 31
Ms 8
museum (m) 7, 38
mushrooms 1
music 25
musician 42

N

name (n) 2, 8, 17
name (v) 17
nationality (ies) 29

near   46
nephew   16
new   8
news   40, 42, 44
newsagent   34
newspaper   44
New Year's Day   38
New Zealand   2
next (next to)   14
niece   16
night-club   3
no thank you   21
non-smoker   5
none   8
north   46
North Sea   30
Norway   2
notepaper   28
novel   45
number   1, 34

O

object   40
odd   18, 38
office   13, 37
old   7
on   14
on board   46
onions   34
opera   42
operator   6
opportunity   37
opposite (opp.)   11, 14, 22
optician   23, 34
orchestra   20, 42
order (n)   2, 43
out   18, 38
outside   14, 40
over   14
own   40

P

pack (of cards)   24
packet   34
Pacific   30
page   17, 44
paint   31
pair   6
pan   6
Panama   2
parcel   40

park   40
part   35
party   36
party-member   6
pass   38
passenger   28
patterned   17
pause   26
pay   40
payment   40
pea   1
peace   27
pear   1
pension   37
people   1, 23
performance   42
person   28
pet   23
Peter Brown   20
pet shop   34
petrol station   35
phone   30
photographer   38
photography   8
picnic   9
picture   15, 32
piece   40
pieces (in pieces)   39
pig   18
pint   34
pipe   41
pity   21
place   12, 40
place of birth   8
plain   17
plant   41
plastic   17
platform   46
play (n)   42
player   28
pleasant   11, 37
please   1, 8, 12
poem   45
poetry   45
police   23
polish   31
pool   15
pop (music)   30
pork   1
port (of embarkation)   46
porter   12
Portugal   2
position   2, 14

position (job)   8
post (v)   31
postman   3
Post Office (PO)   22
pot   6
pound (1 lb)   34
pound note   41
prefix   43
present (n)   24, 36
present (a)   8
President (Pres.)   22
press   44
previous   8
price   19, 40
Prime Minister (PM)   35
prison   39
private   37
problem   23
Professor (Prof.)   10
profit   19
programme   42
psychology   45
pub   30
public telephone   5
punctuation   26
purse   24, 41
put   40
put on   38
puzzle   34

Q

queen   16
question   32
question mark   26
quick   1
quite   29
quiz   40

R

rabbit   14
radio   42, 44
railway   46
railway station   5, 46
raincoat   17
rainy   11
razor   18
read   7, 45
reader   44
rebuild   43
receipt   19, 40
recognize   2

recommend   40
record (n)   24, 40
record (v)   40
record-player   35
record shop   34
reduction   40
referee   8
register   40
rental (car rental)   5
repair   31
reply (RSVP)   22
represent   7
reservation   46
responsibility   37
rest   9
return   46
ride   9
ring (ring for service)   12
road   46
roast   1
roll   1
roof   13, 18
room   5
root   15
rose   34, 41
rough   11
round about   46
row   20
RSVP (please reply)   22
rubbish   41
rucksack   41
rugby   4
run   9
running   4
Russian   29

S

safe   11
sail   4
salad   1
salary   8, 19, 37
Sam   34
sauce   1
saucer   6, 28
sausage   1, 31, 34
save   45
saw (n)   41
scarf   32
scene   9
school   8, 27, 37
science   45
scooter   28

Scottish 29
sculpture 33
sea 27, 40
seat 20
secretary 37
see 40
self-service 37, 43
semi-colon 26
service 1, 23
service charge 38
sew 9
sewing 45
shave 9
sheep 18
sheet 31
ship 46
shirt 17, 24
shoe 24, 34
shoot 3, 9
shop 34
shopping 25, 34
shopping centre 34
shopping list 24
short 37
short-sleeved 17
shower 28
sign (n) 5, 12
signature 8
silk 17
simple 11
sing 42
single 8, 40
sit 40
situation 21, 36
ski 4
skirt (miniskirt) 43
sleeping bag 41
small 34
smile 18
smoker (non-smoker) 5
smooth 11
snack 40
snack bar 30, 35
snooker 4
soap 18
socialist 6
soft 11
solution 23
someone 9
something 40
son 33
sorry 21
spade 24

spaghetti 1
Spain 8
Spanish 8, 29
speed (at full speed) 27
spell 2
spoken 8
spoonful 43
sport 4, 25, 44
squash 4
stadium 18
stage 20, 42
stand 9
star (person) 42
station 5
stationers 34
status 8
stay 40
steal (stolen) 2
stereo 42
steward 16, 46
stewardess 16
stone 7
stop 46
strange 2
strawberry 1, 34, 38
string 18
strong 11
student 45
study 45
subject 6, 45
Sue 24
suffix 43
suit 17
suitcase 24
summer 8
super 25
surprise 21
Susan 25
sweater 17
Sweden 2
sweet (n) 34
sweet (adj) 11
sweet shop 34
swim 9
swimming pool 12

T

table 31
table tennis 4
take off 38
talk 31
tape recorder 3

taste 18, 40
tax 19
teacher 8
team 4, 18
tears 39
teddy bear 24, 25
telephone number 8
television aerial 32
tell 45
tennis 4
terminal 46
test 38
Thailand 2
thank you 21, 36
theatre 20, 38
thick 11
thief (thieves) 32
thin 11
thing 28
thunder storm 6
ticket 40, 46
tie 17
tip 19, 38
title 45
tobacco 41
tobacconist 34
together 41
toilet 5
Tom 25
tomato 1, 38
tool box 41
torch 32
tour 13
towel 18
town (in town) 39
toy 34
traffic 46
train 40
translation 45
transport 37
travel 37, 40, 44
travel agent 34, 37
traveller 28
trip 40
trolley 5
trouble (in trouble) 39
true 9
try on 38
T-shirt 17
Turkey 2
turn 39
TV (television) 42, 44
type 8

typewriter 28, 37

U

uncle 16
uncomfortable 11
under 14
underlining 26
United States of
  America (USA) 2
university (Univ.) 8, 10, 27
unpleasant 11
unusual 43
upstairs 3
us 37
use 32, 40, 43
useless 43
usually 4

V

Value Added Tax (VAT) 10
vanilla 1
vase 31, 41
vet 23
video 42
view 34
village 7
visa 40
visit 36
volume (vol.) 10

W

wage 19
wait 40
waiter 1, 16, 38
waiting room 5
waitress 16
Wales 2
wail 7
wallet 41
wanted 37
war 27
wardrobe 41
warning 40
washing line 32
washing machine 35
wash room 5
wastepaper basket 41
watch 9
water 5, 30, 41
water-skiing 4
way 2, 34

weak   11
wear   40
welcome   40
what's the matter   21
 wheel   15
wife   16
window   32
wine (n)   33
wine-making   45
woman (women)   25, 33
wool   15
word   3, 5, 6
work   23, 27, 37
workers   37
world   2
wound   6, 45
wrap   31
write   4, 8
write out   10
writing   26
wrong   18

X

Xmas (Christmas)   24

Y

young   40
youth hostel   40